Please return/renew this item by the
last date shown to avoid a charge.
Books may also be renewed by phone
and Internet. May not be renewed if
required by another reader.

www.libraries.barnet.gov.uk

BARNET
LONDON BOROUGH

STAR WARS
THE FORCE AWAKENS

CHUCK WENDIG
Writer

LUKE ROSS (Issues #1-2 & #4-6)
MARC LAMING (Issue #3)
Artists

FRANK MARTIN
with **GURU-eFX** (Issue #6)
Colorists

VC's CLAYTON COWLES
Letterer

ESAD RIBIC; MIKE MAYHEW; MIKE DEODATO JR. & FRANK MARTIN;
MIKE DEL MUNDO; RAFAEL ALBUQUERQUE; PAOLO RIVERA
Cover Artists

HEATHER ANTOS
Editor

JORDAN D. WHITE
Supervising Editor

C.B. CEBULSKI
Executive Editor

Based on the screenplay by
LAWRENCE KASDAN & J.J. ABRAMS and MICHAEL ARNDT

For Lucasfilm:

MICHAEL SIGLAIN
Creative Director

FRANK PARISI
Senior Editor

RAYNE ROBERTS, PABLO HIDALGO, LELAND CHEE, MATT MARTIN
Lucasfilm Story Group

COLLECTION EDITOR: **MARK D. BEAZLEY**
ASSOCIATE MANAGING EDITOR: **KATERI WOODY**
ASSOCIATE EDITOR: **SARAH BRUNSTAD**
ASSOCIATE MANAGER, DIGITAL ASSETS: **JOE HOCHSTEIN**
SENIOR EDITOR, SPECIAL PROJECTS: **JENNIFER GRÜNWALD**
VP PRODUCTION & SPECIAL PROJECTS: **JEFF YOUNGQUIST**

LAYOUT: **JEPH YORK**
SVP PRINT, SALES & MARKETING: **DAVID GABRIEL**
EDITOR IN CHIEF: **AXEL ALONSO**
CHIEF CREATIVE OFFICER: **JOE QUESADA**
PUBLISHER: **DAN BUCKLEY**
EXECUTIVE PRODUCER: **ALAN FINE**

FRONT COVER ARTIST: **PHIL NOTO**
BACK COVER ARTIST: **ESAD RIBIC**

THE FORCE AWAKENS #1

A long time ago in a galaxy far,
far away....

Episode VII
THE FORCE AWAKENS

Luke Skywalker has vanished. In his absence, the sinister FIRST ORDER has risen from the ashes of the Empire and will not rest until Skywalker, the last Jedi, has been destroyed.

With the support of the REPUBLIC, General Leia Organa leads a brave RESISTANCE. She is desperate to find her brother Luke and gain his help in restoring peace and justice to the galaxy.

Leia has sent her most daring pilot on a secret mission to Jakku, where an old ally has discovered a clue to Luke's whereabouts....

THIS IS BB-8, LOYAL ASTROMECH DROID TO RESISTANCE PILOT POE DAMERON...

Tuanul Village. The planet of Jakku.

THAT IS POE, KNEELING IN FRONT OF THE DARK FIRST ORDER ENFORCER, KYLO REN.

THE DEAD MAN IS LOR SAN TEKKA, WHO GAVE SOMETHING TO POE--A MAP TO THE LAST JEDI, LUKE SKYWALKER.

SO WHO TALKS FIRST?

YOU TALK FIRST? I TALK FIRST?

THE OLD MAN GAVE IT TO YOU.

IT'S JUST VERY HARD TO UNDERSTAND WITH ALL THE... APPARATUS.

HAVE HIM PUT ON BOARD MY SHUTTLE. WE WILL TAKE HIM TO THE FINALIZER WHERE HE WILL YIELD THE MAP'S LOCATION TO ME.

SIR, THE VILLAGERS?

NO!

KILL THEM ALL.

THIS IS FN-2187. THE BLOOD ON HIS HELMET BELONGED TO HIS FRIEND, FN-2003.

THIS IS REY, A YOUNG SCAVENGER ON JAKKU. FOR HER, EVERY DAY IS THE SAME.

MMM. ONE PORTION.

PAYMENT IS PORTIONS. PORTIONS ARE FOOD. AND IN THE DESERT OF JAKKU, PORTIONS ARE LIFE.

...HALF PORTION.

ONE QUARTER PORTION.

The Goazon Badlands.
Rey's home.

BREEEP!
WOOP!
WOOP!

HUH?

I HAD NO IDEA WE HAD THE BEST PILOT IN THE RESISTANCE ON BOARD.

COMFORTABLE?

...NOT REALLY?

I'M IMPRESSED. NO ONE HAS BEEN ABLE TO GET OUT OF YOU WHAT YOU DID WITH THE MAP.

MIGHT WANNA RETHINK YOUR *TECHNIQUE.*

WHERE...

...IS...

NNNNRRRGGAAAH!

...IT?

IT'S IN A DROID. A BB UNIT.

WELL, THEN. IF IT'S ON JAKKU, WE'LL SOON HAVE IT.

I LEAVE THAT TO YOU, GENERAL HUX.

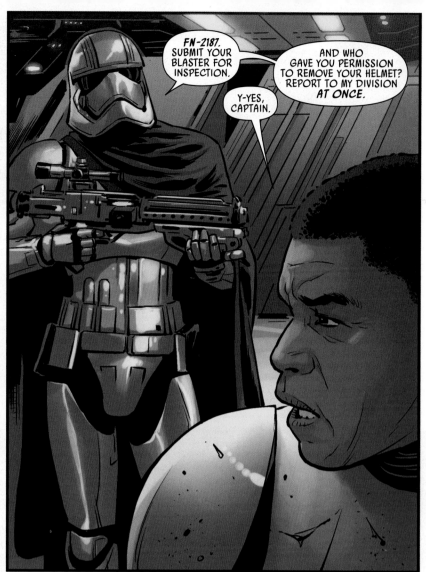

STAY CALM. STAY CALM.

I'M TALKING TO MYSELF.

I AM CALM.

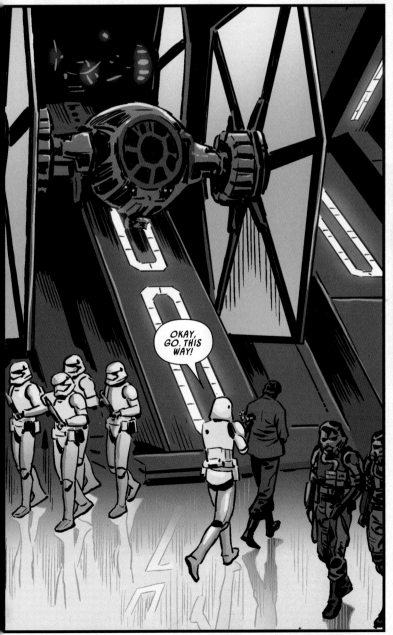

OKAY, GO. THIS WAY!

ALL RIGHT? EVERYBODY COMFORTABLE?

I ALWAYS WANTED TO FLY ONE OF THESE THINGS. CAN YOU SHOOT?

BLASTERS, I CAN.

SAME PRINCIPLE. TOGGLE ON LEFT TO SWITCH BETWEEN MISSILES, CANNONS, MAG PULSE. SIGHTS ON THE RIGHT TO AIM. TRIGGERS TO FIRE.

...THIS IS VERY COMPLICATED.

PWONG

I CAN FIX THIS.

UNSANCTIONED DEPARTURE FROM BAY TWO, SIR.

ALERT GENERAL HUX. STOP THAT FIGHTER!

FA-SHWOOM

TINK

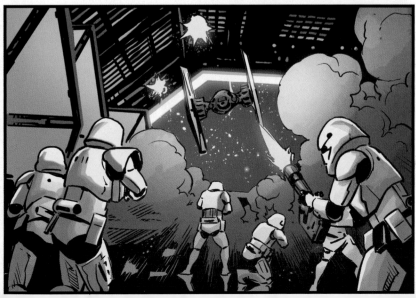

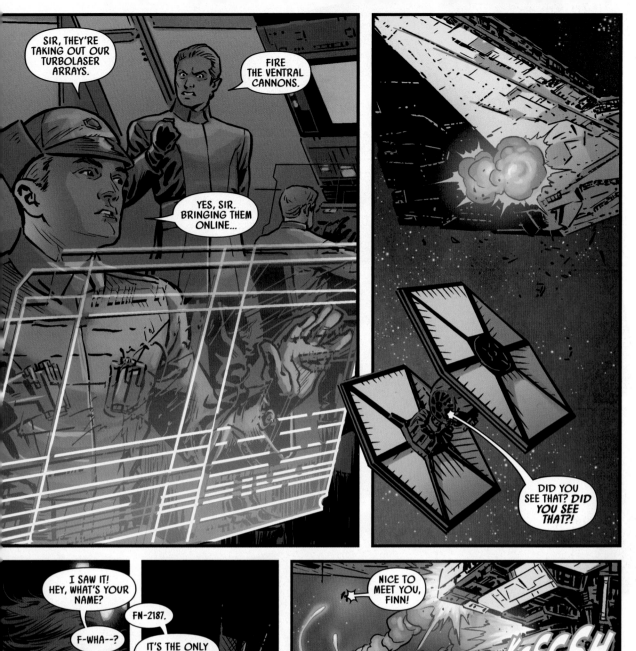

SIR, THEY'RE TAKING OUT OUR TURBOLASER ARRAYS.

FIRE THE VENTRAL CANNONS.

YES, SIR. BRINGING THEM ONLINE...

DID YOU SEE THAT? DID YOU SEE THAT?!

I SAW IT! HEY, WHAT'S YOUR NAME?

FN-2187.

F-WHA--?

IT'S THE ONLY NAME THEY EVER GAVE ME.

WELL, I AIN'T USING IT. FN, HUH? FINN! I'M GONNA CALL YOU FINN. I'M POE DAMERON.

FINN. YEAH, FINN. I LIKE THAT! NICE TO MEET YOU, POE!

NICE TO MEET YOU, FINN!

F'SSSSH

WHERE ARE YOU GOING?!

GOING BACK TO JAKKU, THAT'S WHERE.

NO NO NO! WE CAN'T GO BACK TO JAKKU!

I GOT TO GET TO MY DROID BEFORE THE FIRST ORDER DOES. THAT LITTLE BB UNIT HAS A MAP THAT LEADS STRAIGHT TO LUKE SKYWALKER.

OH, YOU GOTTA BE KIDDING--

IS IT THE RESISTANCE PILOT?

YES, AND HE HAD HELP FROM ONE OF OUR OWN. WE'RE CHECKING THE REGISTERS NOW--

SIR, I--

IT WAS THE ONE FROM THE VILLAGE. FN-2187.

NO PRIOR SIGNS OF NON-CONFORMITY?

THIS WAS HIS...FIRST OFFENSE.

GENERAL! THEY'VE BEEN HIT!

DESTROYED?

DISABLED. THEY WERE HEADED BACK TO JAKKU. THE FIGHTER'S PROJECTED TO CRASH IN THE GOAZON BADLANDS.

THEY WERE GOING BACK FOR THE DROID. SEND A SQUAD TO THE WRECKAGE.

POE!
POE!

COME ON, COME ON...

POE.
NO.

BREEE-WORP!

WELL, DON'T GIVE UP HOPE. HE MIGHT STILL SHOW UP-- WHOEVER IT IS YOU'RE WAITING FOR.

I KNOW ALL ABOUT WAITING.

FOR MY *FAMILY.* THEY'LL BE BACK. ONE DAY.

BWA-WOOP?

WROOOOO

NNNGH. LET ME SEE HERE...ONE HALF PORTION.

LAST WEEK THEY WERE A HALF PORTION *EACH.*

WHAT ABOUT THE *DROID?*

WHAT ABOUT HIM?

I'LL BUY HIM. I'LL PAY...

...NNNGH, SIXTY PORTIONS.

WOOOOO

I....

DROID'S *NOT* FOR SALE. COME ON, BB-8.

FOLLOW THE GIRL. *GET THAT DROID.*

REEP BREEP!

HIM?

ME?

REEP BREEP BEEP!

GET BACK HERE!

GET AWAY FROM ME!

E CHUTA!

FUMP

OOF!

THUD

WHAT'S YOUR HURRY, *THIEF*?

WHAT? THIEF?!

OW! HEY!

BZZT

THE JACKET! THE DROID SAYS YOU *STOLE* IT.

I'VE HAD A PRETTY MESSED-UP DAY, ALL RIGHT? I'D APPRECIATE IF YOU STOPPED ACCUSING ME--

STOP IT!

BZZT

WHERE'D YOU GET IT? IT BELONGS TO HIS *MASTER*.

IT BELONGED TO POE DAMERON. THAT WAS HIS NAME, RIGHT?

BLOOPY BOO!

HE WAS CAPTURED BY THE FIRST ORDER. I HELPED HIM ESCAPE, BUT OUR SHIP CRASHED...

...POE DIDN'T MAKE IT.

THE FORCE AWAKENS #2

Jakku.

NICE SHOT!

I'M GETTING PRETTY GOOD AT THIS!

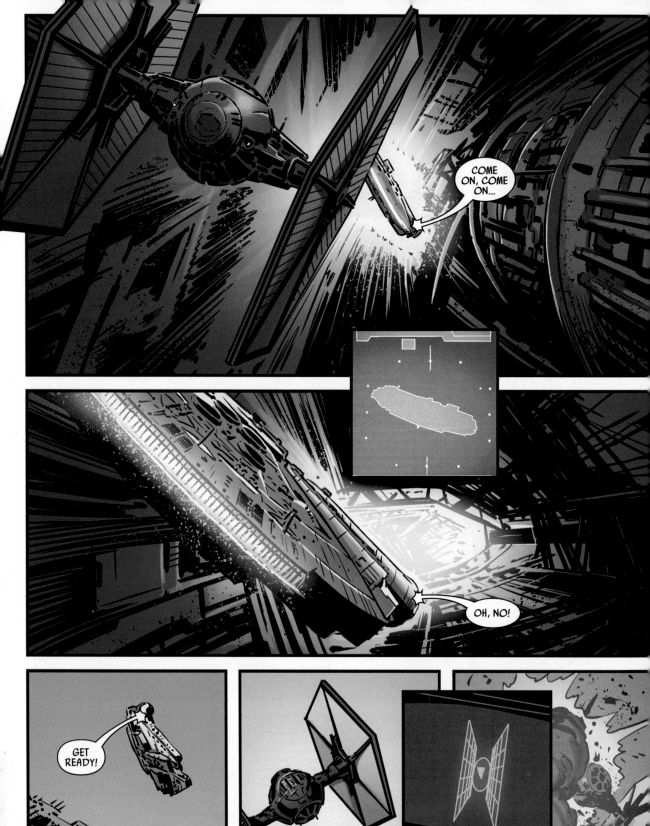

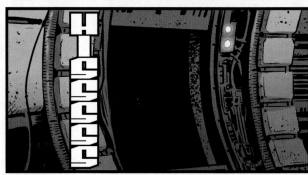

HISSSSSS

CHEWIE... WE'RE HOME.

RRRRAARWRR!

CLANG

WHERE ARE THE OTHERS? WHERE'S THE PILOT?

I'M THE PILOT.

YOU? WHERE'D YOU GET THIS SHIP?

NIIMA OUTPOST.

JAKKU? THAT JUNKYARD?

SEE? JUNKYARD.

I STOLE IT FROM UNKAR PLUTT. HE STOLE IT FROM THE IRVING BOYS, WHO STOLE IT FROM DUCAIN--

WHO STOLE IT FROM ME. YOU TELL HIM THAT HAN SOLO JUST STOLE BACK THE MILLENNIUM FALCON FOR GOOD.

YOU *ARE* THE HAN SOLO WHO FOUGHT WITH THE REBELLION. YOU *KNEW* HIM.

YEAH, I KNEW HIM. I KNEW LUKE.

KA-CHUNGGG

DON'T TELL ME A RATHTAR HAS GOTTEN LOOSE--

DID YOU JUST SAY RATHTARS?

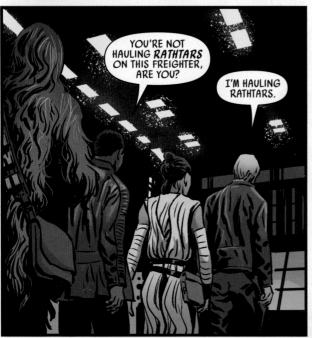

YOU'RE NOT HAULING *RATHTARS* ON THIS FREIGHTER, ARE YOU?

I'M HAULING RATHTARS.

OH, *GREAT.* IT'S THE GUAVIAN DEATH GANG. MUST'VE TRACKED US FROM NANTOON.

BALA-TIK, WHAT'S THE PROBLEM?

WE WANT OUR MONEY BACK.

I HEARD YOU ALSO BORROWED FIFTY THOUSAND FROM KANJIKLUB.

THEY HAVE BLASTERS!

A LOT OF 'EM.

YOU KNOW YOU CAN'T TRUST THOSE LITTLE FREAKS. BESIDES, YOU THINK HUNTING RATHTARS IS CHEAP? I *SPENT* ALL THAT MONEY.

KANJIKLUB WANTS THEIR INVESTMENT BACK, TOO.

I NEVER MADE A DEAL WITH KANJIKLUB!

TELL THAT TO KANJIKLUB.

TASU LEECH. GOOD TO SEE YOU.

KUPRAKEI, MADAGAN SHIMA, SOLO.*

BOYS, YOU'RE BOTH GONNA GET WHAT I PROMISED-- HAVE I EVER NOT DELIVERED FOR YOU BEFORE?

*No, it's not. It's over, Solo.

YEAH.

DAKRI.*

*Twice.

YOUR GAME IS OLD. THERE'S NO ONE IN THE GALAXY LEFT FOR YOU TO SWINDLE.

THAT BB UNIT. THE FIRST ORDER IS LOOKING FOR ONE JUST LIKE IT. AND TWO FUGITIVES.

SEARCH THE FREIGHTER!

IF WE CLOSE THE BLAST DOORS IN THAT CORRIDOR, WE CAN TRAP BOTH GANGS.

RESETTING THE FUSES SHOULD DO IT...

CLOSE THE BLAST DOORS FROM HERE? HOW?

FZZT

FZZT

FZZT

I GOT A BAD FEELING ABOUT THIS.

OH, NO. WRONG FUSES.

KILL THEM! AND TAKE THAT DROID!

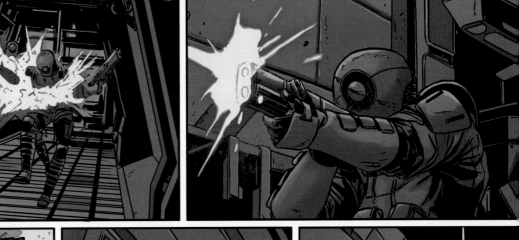

CLOSE THE RAMP BEHIND US!

SOMEONE TAKE CARE OF CHEWIE!

WHERE'RE YOU GOING?

UNKAR PLUTT INSTALLED A FUEL PUMP. IF WE DON'T PRIME THAT, WE'RE NOT GOING ANYWHERE.

AND YOU COULD USE A CO-PILOT.

FINE, JUST WATCH THE THRUST--WE'RE GOING OUT OF HERE AT LIGHTSPEED.

WHAT? FROM INSIDE THE HANGAR?

HAN, IS THAT EVEN POSSIBLE?

I NEVER ASK THAT QUESTION UNTIL AFTER I'VE DONE IT.

INFORM THE FIRST ORDER THAT HAN SOLO HAS THE DROID.

AND IT'S ON BOARD THE *MILLENNIUM FALCON.*

THERE HAS BEEN AN AWAKENING. HAVE YOU FELT IT?

YES.

THERE'S SOMETHING MORE.

THE DROID WE SEEK IS ABOARD THE *MILLENNIUM FALCON*, IN THE HANDS OF YOUR FATHER.

HAN SOLO.

...

HE MEANS *NOTHING* TO ME.

EVEN *YOU*, MASTER OF THE KNIGHTS OF REN, HAVE NEVER FACED SUCH A TEST.

BY THE GRACE OF YOUR TRAINING, I WILL NOT BE SEDUCED.

WE SHALL SEE. *WE SHALL SEE.*

THIS MAP'S NOT COMPLETE.

IT'S JUST A PIECE. EVER SINCE LUKE DISAPPEARED, PEOPLE HAVE BEEN LOOKIN' FOR HIM.

WHY DID HE LEAVE?

HE WAS TRAINING A NEW GENERATION OF JEDI.

ONE BOY, AN APPRENTICE, TURNED AGAINST HIM, DESTROYED IT ALL. LUKE FELT RESPONSIBLE. HE JUST...

...WALKED AWAY FROM EVERYTHING.

DO YOU KNOW WHAT HAPPENED TO HIM?

A LOT OF RUMORS. STORIES. THE PEOPLE WHO KNEW HIM BEST THINK HE WENT LOOKING FOR THE FIRST JEDI TEMPLE.

THE JEDI WERE REAL?

USED TO WONDER THAT MYSELF. THOUGHT IT WAS JUST A BUNCH OF MUMBO JUMBO.

MAGICAL POWER HOLDING TOGETHER GOOD AND EVIL? THE DARK SIDE AND THE LIGHT?

CRAZY THING IS, IT'S ALL TRUE. THE FORCE. THE JEDI.

ALL OF IT.

YOU WANT MY HELP? WELL, YOU'RE GETTING IT.

GONNA SEE AN OLD FRIEND. SHE'LL GET YOUR DROID HOME.

LET'S GO.

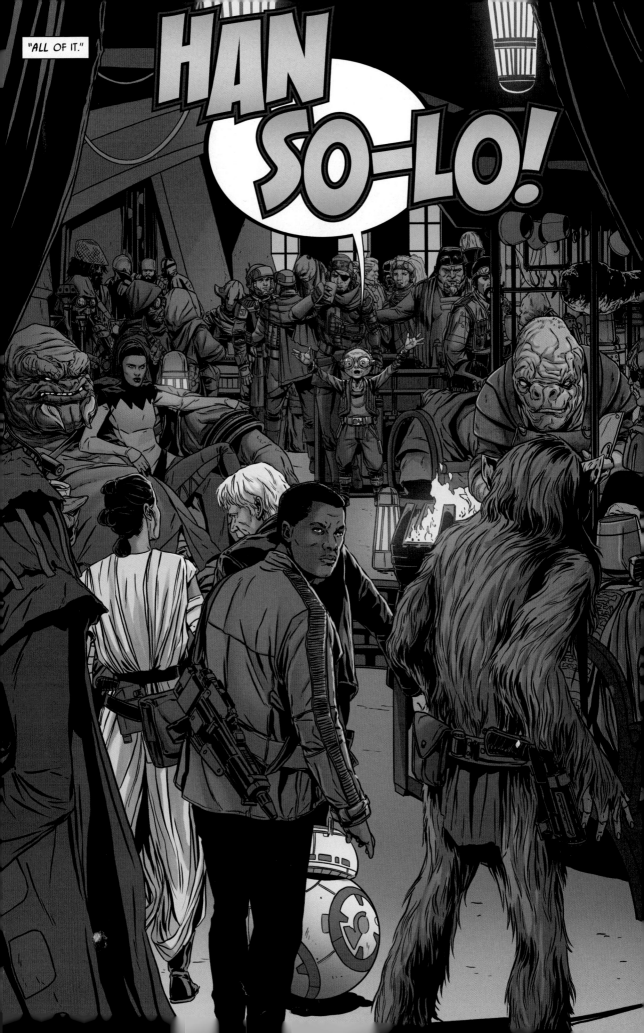

A MAP TO SKYWALKER HIMSELF? YOU'RE RIGHT BACK IN THE MESS.

MAZ, I NEED YOU TO GET THIS DROID TO LEIA.

MMM, NO.

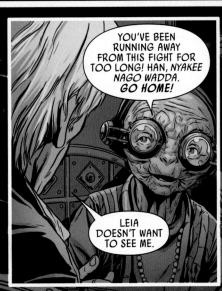

YOU'VE BEEN RUNNING AWAY FROM THIS FIGHT FOR TOO LONG! HAN, NYAKEE NAGO WADDA. GO HOME!

LEIA DOESN'T WANT TO SEE ME.

PLEASE. WE CAME HERE FOR YOUR HELP.

WHAT FIGHT?

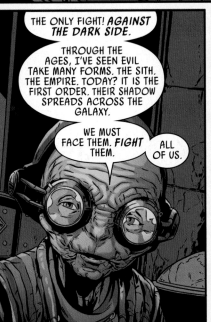

THE ONLY FIGHT! AGAINST THE DARK SIDE.

THROUGH THE AGES, I'VE SEEN EVIL TAKE MANY FORMS. THE SITH. THE EMPIRE. TODAY? IT IS THE FIRST ORDER. THEIR SHADOW SPREADS ACROSS THE GALAXY.

WE MUST FACE THEM. FIGHT THEM. ALL OF US.

THERE IS NO FIGHT AGAINST THE FIRST ORDER! NOT ONE WE CAN WIN.

SOLO, WHAT'S SHE DOING?

I DUNNO. BUT IT AIN'T GOOD.

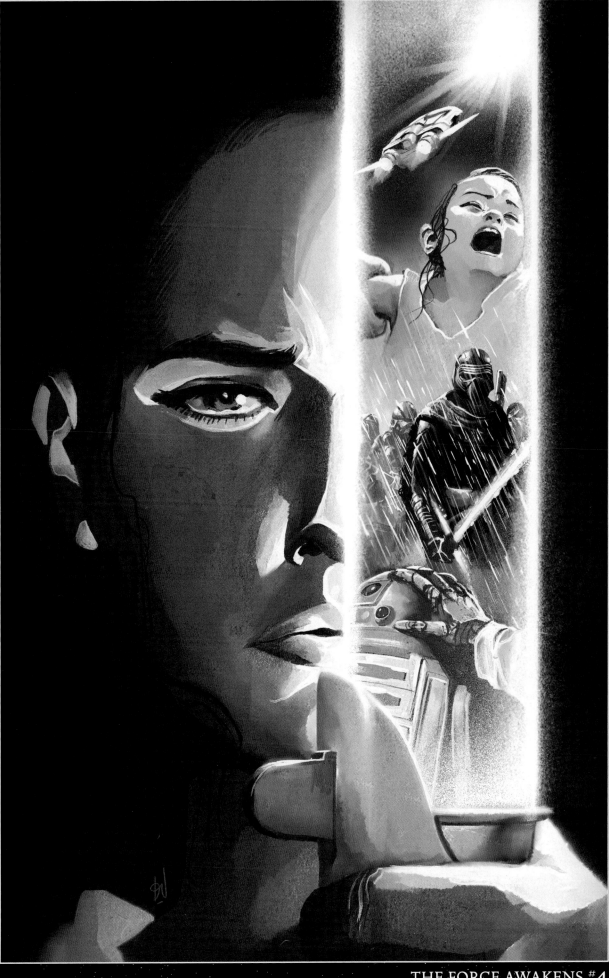

THE FORCE AWAKENS #4

REY...

...THESE ARE YOUR...

...FIRST...

...STEPS...

WHAT WAS THAT?

I... I SHOULDN'T HAVE GONE IN THERE...

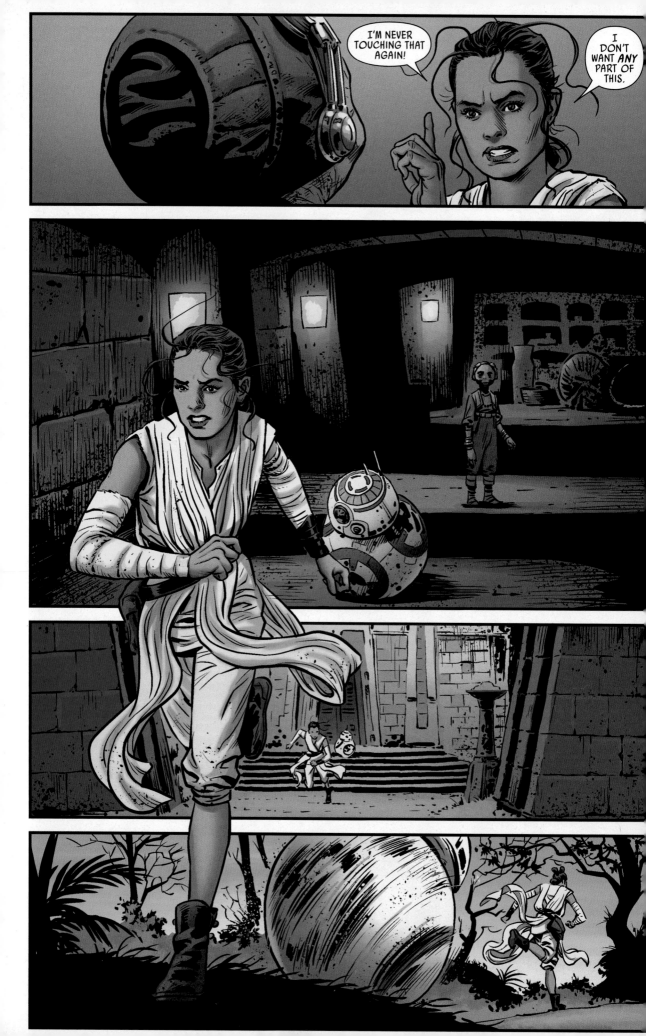

The Hosnian System.

HOSNIAN PRIME: CURRENT CAPITAL OF THE NEW REPUBLIC (AND HOME TO THE SENATE).

LANEVER VILLECHAM, CHANCELLOR OF THE REPUBLIC.

KORR SELLA, REPUBLIC COMMANDER AND AIDE TO GENERAL LEIA ORGANA.

I'VE HAD THIS FOR AGES.

KEPT IT LOCKED AWAY.

WHERE'D YOU GET THAT, MAZ?

A GOOD QUESTION, HAN-- FOR ANOTHER TIME.

TAKE IT! FIND YOUR FRIEND!

RRAWRRAWR!

THOSE BEASTS!

THEY'RE HERE!

RRRUMMMBLE

CHOOM

REY AND BEEBEE-ATE. THEY NEED YOU, FINN!

GO.

YOU *HAVE* ONE!

I NEED A WEAPON.

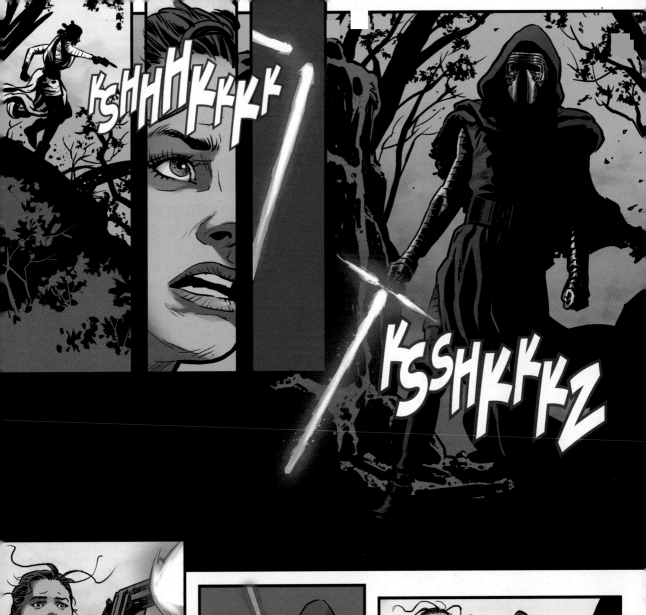

KSHHKKKI

KSSHKKKZ

THE GIRL I'VE HEARD SO MUCH ABOUT.

THE DROID. WHERE IS IT?

WAIT.

YOU'VE SEEN IT.

THE MAP.

SIR! RESISTANCE FIGHTERS! WE NEED MORE TROOPS.

PULL THE DIVISION. FORGET THE DROID.

WE HAVE WHAT WE NEED.

NO.
NO, NO, NO!

NO! REY!

REYYYY!

HE TOOK HER! SHE'S *GONE!*

YEAH. YEAH...I *KNOW...*

LOOK WHO IT IS! DID YOU SEE WHO--? OH.

EXCUSE ME, PRINC--

UH, *GENERAL.* SORRY.

HAN.

I SAW HIM, *LEIA.*

I SAW OUR *SON.*

GENERAL ORGANA, I REGRET TO INFORM YOU, BUT THIS MAP RECOVERED FROM BEEBEE-ATE IS ONLY PARTIALLY COMPLETE.

IT MATCHES NO CHARTED SYSTEM ON RECORD.

IT IS VERY DOUBTFUL THAT ARTOO WOULD HAVE THE REST OF THE MAP IN HIS BACKUP DATA.

WE SIMPLY DO NOT HAVE ENOUGH INFORMATION TO LOCATE MASTER LUKE.

CAN'T BELIEVE I WAS SO *FOOLISH* TO THINK I COULD FIND LUKE AND BRING HIM HOME.

LEIA--

DON'T DO THAT, HAN.

DO WHAT?

ANYTHING!

I'M TRYING TO BE HELPFUL!

WHEN DID THAT EVER HELP? AND *DON'T* SAY THE DEATH STAR--

LISTEN TO ME, WILL YA?

WHERE AM I?

YOU'RE MY GUEST.

...YOU STILL WANT TO KILL ME, DON'T YOU?

THAT HAPPENS WHEN YOU'RE BEING HUNTED BY A *CREATURE* IN A *MASK.*

KSSSSSS

TELL ME ABOUT THE DROID.

HE'S A BB UNIT WITH A SELENIUM DRIVE AND A THERMAL HYPERSCAN VINDICATOR--

HE'S CARRYING A SECTION OF A NAVIGATIONAL CHART. BUT WE NEED THE LAST PIECE.

SOMEHOW YOU CONVINCED THE DROID TO SHOW IT TO YOU.

YOU. A *SCAVENGER.*

YOU KNOW, I CAN TAKE WHATEVER I WANT.

Starkiller Base.

NO.

KZZZSH

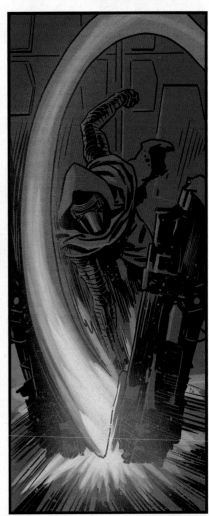

BEGIN CHARGING THE WEAPON!

YES, SIR. WEAPON CHARGING.

SANITATION?

THEN HOW DO YOU KNOW HOW TO DISABLE THE SHIELDS?

I DON'T. I'M JUST HERE TO GET REY.

PEOPLE ARE COUNTING ON US! THE *GALAXY* IS COUNTING ON US!

SOLO, WE'LL FIGURE IT OUT. WE'LL USE THE *FORCE*.

THAT'S NOT HOW THE FORCE WORKS!

THE LONGER WE'RE HERE, THE LESS LUCK WE'RE GOING TO HAVE. HOW ARE WE GOING TO GET THE SHIELDS DOWN?

I HAVE AN IDEA ABOUT THAT...

RAAAWWR!

"THERE'S STILL LIGHT IN HIM...

"YOU'RE HIS *FATHER*..."

BEN!

HAN SOLO.

I'VE BEEN WAITING FOR THIS DAY FOR A LONG TIME.

TAKE OFF THAT MASK. YOU DON'T *NEED* IT.

THE FACE OF MY SON.

WHAT DO YOU THINK YOU'LL SEE IF I DO?

THUD

YOUR SON IS GONE. HE WAS WEAK AND FOOLISH LIKE HIS FATHER.

SO I DESTROYED HIM.

SNOKE IS USING YOU FOR YOUR POWER. WHEN HE GETS WHAT HE WANTS, HE'LL CRUSH YOU.

...IT'S TOO LATE.

VWOMMZ

THAT LIGHTSABER. IT BELONGS TO ME!

COME GET IT, REN.

KSSSH

GUH!

RAAAAH!

KZLSSSSH

KZLSSSSH

KZLSSSSH

AAAAAAAAAHHH!

RRRUMBLE

FINN!

HISSSSS

Issue #1 variant by Phil Noto

Issue #1 variant by John
Cassaday & Paul Mounts

Issue #1 variant by Joe
Quesada & Richard Isanove

Issue #2 variant by Chris
Samnee & Matt Wilson

Issue #5 Action Figure variant
by John Tyler Christopher

Issue #6 variant by Esad Ribic